D1599568

Submarines of the Tsarist Navy

The *Akula,* one of the most capable submarines of the tsarist fleet. The armored cruiser *Rurik* is under way in the background.

SUBMARINES
of the Tsarist Navy

⚓ A PICTORIAL HISTORY ⚓

Edited by I. D. Spassky and V. P. Semyonov
with Norman Polmar

NAVAL INSTITUTE PRESS   Annapolis, Maryland

Library of Congress Cataloging-in-Publication Data
Submarines of the tsarist navy : a pictorial history / edited by I. D. Spassky
    and V. P. Semyonov ; with Norman Polmar.
            p.   cm.
      Includes index.
      ISBN 1-55750-771-6 (alk. paper)
        1. Submarines (Ships)—Russia—History—Pictorial works.
    2. Russia. Voennyi flot—Submarine forces—History.   I. Spassky,
    I. D. II. Semyonov, V. P. III. Polmar, Norman.
    V859.R8S83   1996
    623.8 ' 2572 ' 094709041—dc20   95-44039
    Printed in the United States of America on acid-free paper ∞

05 04 03 02 01 00 99 98   9 8 7 6 5 4 3 2

First printing

Unless noted otherwise, photographs for *Submarines of the Tsarist Navy* are from
the collections of Russian State Naval Archives; Central Design Bureau for
Marine Engineering Rubin; Norman Polmar; and Captain 1st Rank Vadim
Yuryevich Usov, Soviet Navy (Retired).

Dedicated to the 300th anniversary
of the Russian Navy (1696–1996)
and to the 90th anniversary of the
Russian Submarine Fleet (1903–1993)

❖ Contents ❖

Submarines of the Tsarist Navy

⚜ Perspective ⚜

The purpose of *Submarines of the Tsarist Navy* is to familiarize Western readers with one of the important stages in the history of the Russian submarine fleet in the period before the Revolution of 1917.

Having accomplished in the late 19th century a complicated and interesting stage of determining the feasibility of creating submarines, Russia entered the 20th century designing its first combat submarine through the efforts of several gifted engineers and inventors—among them, K. A. Shilder, I. F. Aleksandrovsky, and S. K. Dzhevetskiy should be specifically mentioned. Although not resulting in complete successes, their efforts enabled Russia to accumulate sufficient design experience, together with achievements in adjacent fields of engineering—internal combustion engines and electrical systems—to allow the Russians to pass from experiments to the construction of operational submarines.

On 13 May 1901, I. G. Bubnov and M. N. Beklemishev submitted to the Navy Ministry the design of "Torpedo boat No. 113," the first designation given to the submarine *Delfin*. The design was approved, and on 5 July 1901, the Baltic Shipbuilding & Engine Works in St. Petersburg received the order to build the submarine of this design.[1]

In 1903 her trials were completed, and the *Delfin* joined the Russian Navy. That event marked the beginning of a period of intensive development of the

---

1. St. Petersburg was renamed Petrograd from 1914 to 1924, and Leningrad from then until 1991, when the city reverted to the name St. Petersburg.

Russian submarine fleet. Sixty-nine submarines entered the Russian Navy from 1903 to 1918; eight more submarines ordered by the Navy were left unfinished in 1918. (From that year until 1926 there was a period of inactivity in Russian submarine development.)

During this period of 15 years Russia acquired 34 submarines built to native designs. Thirty-two of them were designed by Ivan Grigorievich Bubnov, who can be called, by modern terminology, the General Designer of the Russian Navy. Battleships were also built to his designs. But there were other designers who produced remarkable designs—S. K. Dzhevetskiy designed the submarine *Pochtovy,* which was fitted with a single engine to provide propulsive power for both surface and submerged operation, and M. P. Nalyotov designed the *Krab,* the world's first underwater minelayer. In addition, 16 submarines were built in Russian shipyards to the designs of Americans—four to plans drawn up by Simon Lake and 12 to those of John P. Holland.

In this intensive era of submarine development, the Russian Navy procured 23 submarines abroad:

- Three submarines were purchased from the Krupp firm in Germany— the *Karp, Karas,* and *Kambala;* this was such a profitable order that the Krupp firm presented Russia with the submarine *Forel.*
- The *Protector* (renamed *Osetr*) and five additional submarines of this type were purchased from the American firm of Simon Lake. All six were built by Newport News Shipbuilding and Dry Dock Company, with five completed at Libau under Lake's guidance.
- Twelve submarines were delivered from the American firm of Holland— the *Fulton,* renamed *Som,* and 11 units of the project called "AG," or *Amerikanskiy Golland* (American Holland). The construction of five of these submarines was completed by the Baltic Shipbuilding & Engine Works in St. Petersburg, and six were built by the Baltic Works Subsidiary in Nikolayev on the Black Sea. Only two of the later submarines were built by 1918, but they were not commissioned in the Tsarist fleet; the remainder were completed by the Soviet government after the Russian Revolution and Civil War.
- One submarine—the *Svyatoi Georgy*—was purchased from the Italian firm Fiat.

The contribution of Russian enterprises in the creation of the submarine fleet is reflected in Table 1.

The combat baptism of Russian submarines occurred during the Russo-Japanese War of 1904–1905. Thirteen submarines were transferred by railroad

Table 1 Submarine Designers and Builders

| WORKS | INDIGENOUS DESIGNS | | | | | | | | AMERICAN DESIGNS | | | | TOTAL |
| | BUBNOV | | | | | | DZHEVETSKIY | NALYOTOV | LAKE | | HOLLAND | | |
	Delfin	Kasatka	Minoga	Akula	Morzh	Bars	Pochtovy	Krab	Kaiman	Shchuka	Narval	No. 1	
Baltic Shipbuilding* & Engine Works, St Petersburg	1	6	1	1	—	6***	—	—	—	—	—	—	15
Metallicheskiy Works, St. Petersburg	—	—	—	—	—	—	1	—	—	—	—	—	1
Crighton Works, St. Petersburg	—	—	—	—	—	—	—	—	4	—	—	—	4
Nevskiy Shipbuilding & Machine Works, St. Petersburg	—	—	—	—	—	—	—	—	—	6	—	3	9
Nobel & Lessner, Revel	—	—	—	—	—	10**	—	—	—	—	—	—	10
Baltic Works Subsidiary, Nikolayev**	—	—	—	—	3	2	—	—	—	—	—	—	5
Nevskiy Works Subsidiary, St. Petersburg	—	—	—	—	—	—	—	—	—	—	3	—	3
Chantier Naval, Kikolayev	—	—	—	—	—	2**	—	1	—	—	—	—	3
												TOTAL	50

* The Baltic Shipbuilding & Engine Works completed five submarines of the AG class.

** The Baltic Works Subsidiary in Nikolayev completed six submarines of the AG class.

*** One submarine of the Bars class was left unfinished at the Baltic Shipbuilding & Engine Works, one submarine at Nobel & Lessner Works, and two submarines of this type at Chantier Naval.

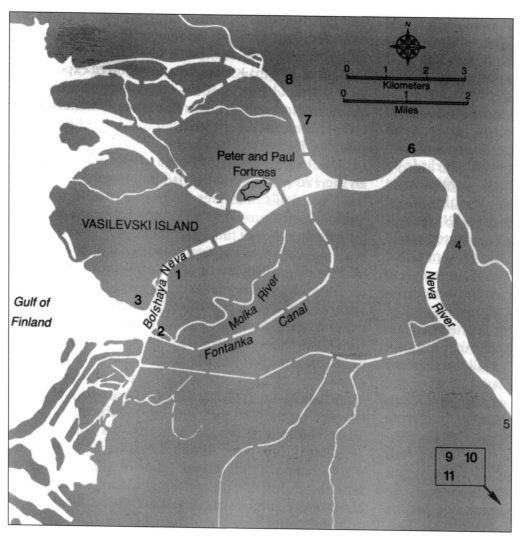

St. Petersburg-Petrograd submarine building yards: (1) Galerny Island, site of the New Admiralty Yard since 1800; renamed Sudomekh in 1931, and New Admiralty Yard in 1957. (2) Galerny islet, site of the Admiralty Shipyard; renamed the Marti Yard in 1922, and again Admiralty Yard in 1957; merged with Sudomekh-New Admiralty in 1972 to form the United Admiralty Association. (3) Baltisky (Baltic) Shipyard. (4) Okhtinskoye Admiralty; from the end of the 19th century until 1913, the yard was leased by the firm Craton & Company; later Petrozavod Yard. (5) Nevsky Foundry and Mechanical Works established in 1837 (also known as Semyannikovsky Works); since 1922 known as the Nevsky Plant named after V. I. Lenin. (6) St. Petersburg Metal Works, established in 1857; later Leningrad Metal Works. (7) Nobel Works, established in 1840; later Russian Diesel. (8) Lessner Works, established in 1853. (9) Aleksandrovsky Works; later Proletarsky. (10) Izhorsky Works. (11) Obukhov Works; later Bolshevik Works.

from the St. Petersburg area to Vladivostok in the Far East for combat operations. The first submarine that entered combat was the *Som,* which attacked Japanese destroyers on 28 April 1905, but the destroyers had noticed the submarine and left the danger area. The Russian Navy was highly criticized for the lack of use of its submarine force during the Russo-Japanese War. The employment of the submarines, however, was limited by their inadequate technical capabilities.

Russian submarines entered World War I more prepared and successfully conducted a number of reconnaissance, offensive, and defensive operations at the Baltic and Black Seas. The submarines *Volk, Vepr, Tyulen, Morzh,* and *Kashalot* achieved the best results in combat operations.[2] In addition, nine British submarines—five of the "E" series and four of the "C" series—actively participated in combat operations of the Russian Baltic Fleet during World War I.[3]

Table 2   Russian Submarine Losses, 1914–1917

NAME	DATE	CIRCUMSTANCES OF THE LOSS
BALTIC SEA-GULF OF FINLAND		
Akula	Nov 1915	Lost on mission to Memel
Som	23 May 1916	Rammed by the Swedish steamer Argermanland
*Lvitsa**	June 1917	Lost on combat mission
*AG-14***	1917	Lost on combat mission
*Bars**	May 1917	Lost on combat mission
*Gepard**	Oct 1917	Lost on combat mission
BLACK SEA		
Morzh	May 1917	Lost on combat mission in the area of the Bosporus

  * One of these three submarines was discovered in 1993 by Swedish investigators east of the island of Gotske Sandoen at a depth of 120 meters.
** Some Holland submarines carried numbers instead of names, i.e., AG for *Amerikanskiy Golland.*

2. A detailed English-language account of Russian submarine operations in World War I is in Norman Polmar and Jurrien Noot, *Submarines of the Russian and Soviet Navies, 1718–1990* (Annapolis, Md.: Naval Institute Press, 1991). Also see George Nekrasov, *North of Gallipoli: The Black Sea Fleet at War 1914–1917* (Boulder, Colo.: East European Monographs [distributed by Columbia University Press], 1992).

3. A recent description of the British submarine operations in the Baltic Sea is Michael Wilson, *Baltic Assignment: British Submarines in Russia, 1914–1919* (London: Leo Cooper, 1985).

Revolutionary sailors march on the jetty alongside the submarine depot ship *Dvina* on Easter Sunday 1917. Russian sailors were in the forefront of the revolutions of 1906 and 1917, the second of which toppled the tsarist regime in Russia.

During the war period, five submarines were purchased from the American firm Holland, four of which were completed after the Revolution of 1917. These submarines served in the Soviet Navy up to the Great Patriotic War of 1941–1945 and successfully carried out combat operations at the Black Sea during that conflict.[4]

During the World War I period, from 1914 to 1917, seven Russian submarines were lost (Table 2).

4. "Great Patriotic War" is the Russian term for the Soviet participation in World War II in Europe, from June 1941 through May 1945.

❖ Designers ❖

Designer I. F. Aleksandrovsky

Aleksandrovsky-designed submarine, 1866.

7

Designer S. K. Dzhevetskiy

Dzhevetskiy-designed submarine at Port Arthur in the Far East. Two dynamite mines could be carried externally.

Dzhevetskiy-designed submarine of the No. 3 type, of which 50 were built in 1879–1881.

Designer I. G. Bubnov.

The *Delfin*, designed by Bubnov and M. N. Beklemishev.

The *Delfin* under way.

Designer M. N. Beklemishev.

The *Delfin*—Russia's first "modern" submarine.

The *Kasatka*, designed
by I. G. Bubnov and M. N.
Beklemishev.

Designer John P. Holland.

The *Sudak* of the Holland-designed *Som* class showing the narrow deck and side, or "saddle," ballast tanks on the starboard side.

Simon Lake. (U.S. National Archives)

The Lake-designed *Krokodil* of the *Alligator* class.

Communications engineer and submarine designer
M. P. Nalyotov.

The stern of the *Krab*.

❖ Submarine Characteristics ❖

Delfin

Name	Built[5]
Delfin	1903

Displacement: 113 tons surfaced
124 tons submerged
Diving depth: 50 m
Dimensions: length 19.6 m
beam 3.35 m
draft 2.9 m
Propulsion: 1 gasoline engine; 300 hp; surface speed 10 knots
1 electric motor; 120 hp; underwater speed 5 to 6 knots
Armament: 2 torpedoes in external Dzhevetskiy drop-collar torpedo
launchers
Complement: 20

The *Delfin* was the first Russian combat submarine. It was built by the Baltic Shipbuilding & Engine Works in St. Petersburg to the design of I. G. Bubnov and M. N. Beklemishev.

The submarine was decommissioned in Arkhangelsk in August 1917.

5. Year completed.

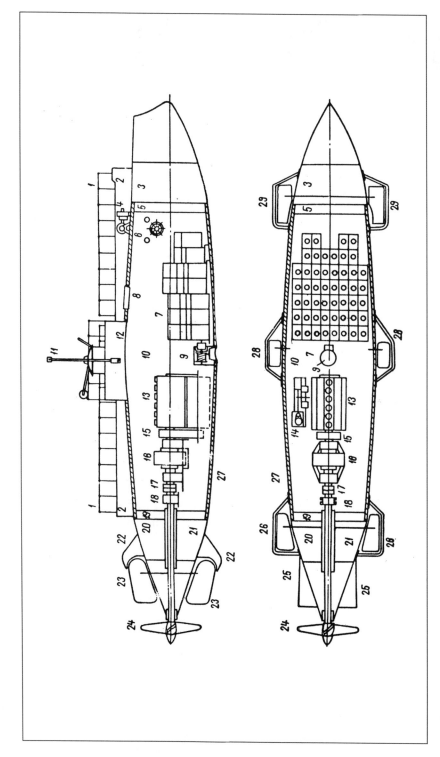

Delfin class. 1. handrail; 2. super structure; 3. bow main ballast tank; 4. capstan of the surface anchor; 5. bow trim tank; 6. bow horizontal rudder control post; 7. battery; 8. hatch for loading batteries; 9. shield for the submerged anchor; 10. inner volume of the solid hull; 11. periscope; 12. conning tower; 13. gasoline motor; 14. compressor and hold with overall electrical drive; 15. transfer to the shaft from the motor; 16. electrical propeller engine; 17. coupling; 18. thrust bearing; 19. and 20. stern trim tank; 21. stern main ballast tank; 22. fairwater of the vertical rudder; 23. vertical rudder; 24. screw propeller; 25. horizontal stabilizer; 26. stern horizontal rudders; 27. solid hull; 28. middle horizontal rudders; 29. bow horizontal rudders

The *Delfin* at dockside. In spite of several accidents, the craft was considered a success and is rated as Russia's first "combatant" submarine.

Kasatka Class

Name	Built
Kasatka (killer whale)	1904
Skat (ray)	1904
Nalim (burbot)	1904
Fieldmarshal Graf (Count) Sheremetev	1904
Makrel (mackerel)	1905
Okun (perch)	1905

Displacement:	140 tons surfaced
	177 tons submerged
Diving depth:	50 m
Dimensions:	length 33.5 m
	beam 3.35 m
	draft 3.4 m
Propulsion:	1 gasoline engine; 120 hp; surface speed 8.5 knots
	1 electric motor; 100 hp; underwater speed 5.5 knots
Armament:	4 torpedoes in external Dzhevetskiy drop-collar torpedo launchers
	1 machine gun (during the war the submarines *Nalim* and *Skat* were equipped with 1 37-mm gun)
Complement:	25

These boats were built by the Baltic Shipbuilding & Engine Works in St. Petersburg to the design of I. G. Bubnov.

The submarines *Okun* and *Makrel* were modernized in 1905, being refitted with a dynamo-diesel engine of 120 horsepower that supplied power to the main propulsion electric motor.

The *Kasatka* was decommissioned in 1925; the *Skat* and *Nalim* were scuttled in Sevastopol in 1919. The *Makrel* was decommissioned in 1925, the *Okun* in 1925, and the *Fieldmarshal Graf Sheremetev* sank in Petrograd in 1922.

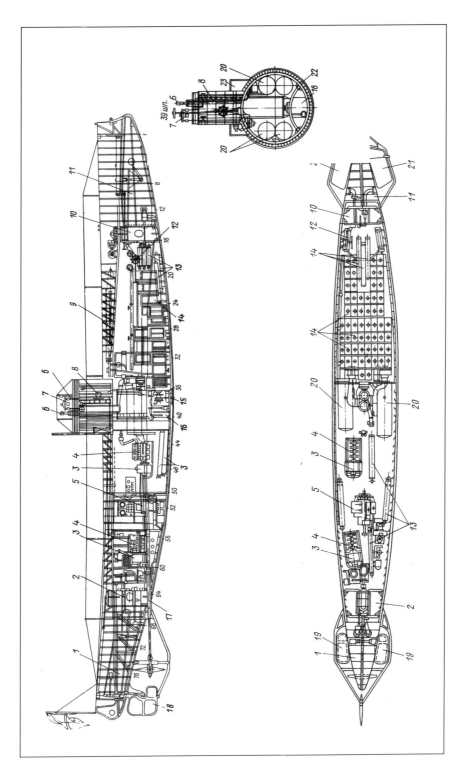

Kasatka. 1. stern main ballast tank; 2. stern trim tank; 3. dynamo engine (electric generator); 4. gasoline engine; 5. propeller engine; 6. periscope; 7. entrance hatch; 8. control for the vertical rudder; 9. Dzhevetskiy apparatus with a torpedo; 10. bow trim tank; 11. bow ballast tank; 12. control for the bow horizontal rudders; 13. tank for compressed air; 14. batteries; 15. submerged anchor; 16. middle (separating) tank; 17. propeller shaft; 18. rudder plane; 19. stern horizontal rudders; 20. fuel tanks; 21. bow horizontal rudders; 22. wooden border on the hull; 23. flooding superstructure

The *Kasatka* before completion.

The submarines *Delfin* (left) and *Kasatka* under tow.

The submarine *Nalim* of the *Kasatka* class.

Okun of the *Kasatka* class; note spaces for the Dzhevetskiy drop-collar torpedo launchers, two per side.

Kasatka-class submarine showing torpedoes in place for Dzhevetskiy launchers.

From left: *Delfin*, *Fieldmarshal Graf Sheremetev*, *Skat*, and *Nalim*.

Forel

Name	Built
Forel (trout)	1904

Displacement:	17 tons surfaced
	18 tons submerged
Diving depth:	30 m
Dimensions:	length 13.0 m
	beam 2.8 m
	draft 1.7 m
Propulsion:	1 electric motor; 65 hp; surface speed 6.6 knots/underwater speed 6.5 knots
Armament:	2 torpedoes in external torpedo tubes
Complement:	4

The *Forel* was built by Krupp in Germany by the design of R. d'Equevilley-Montjustin. The craft was presented to Russia on obtaining the Russian order for three submarines (*Karp*, *Karas*, and *Kambala*).

The *Forel* was propelled by an electric motor both on the surface and submerged.

The submarine *Forel* was decommissioned in 1911.

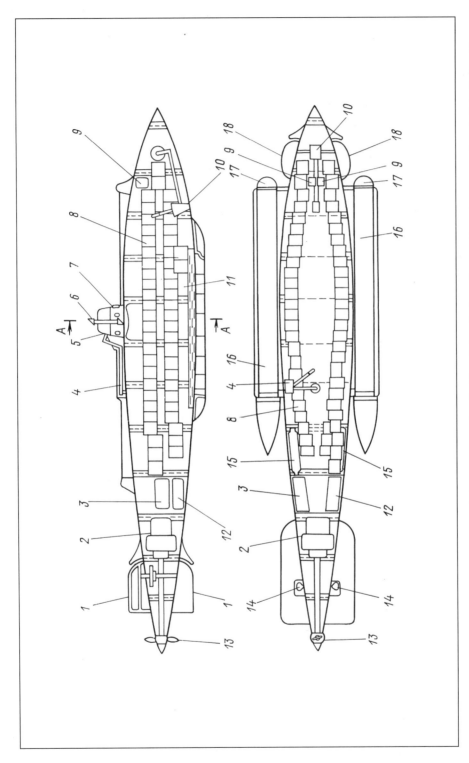

Forel. 1. vertical rudder; 2. propeller engine; 3. ballast pump; 4. hatch drive; 5. hatch; 6. periscope; 7. main command post; 8. batteries; 9. electrical drives to the covering of the torpedo apparatus; 10. drive for the horizontal rudder; 11. ballast tank; 12. compressor; 13. screw propeller; 14. stern horizontal rudder; 15. air storage; 16. and 17. torpedo and covering; 18. bow horizontal rudder; 19. superstructure; 20. casing of the hatch drive; 21. vertical rudder drive

The *Forel.*

The *Forel*, a gift to Russia from the Krupp shipyard in Germany, in appreciation for a Russian submarine order.

Karp Class

Name	Built
Karp	1907
Karas (crucian carp)	1907
Kambala (flounder)	1907

Displacement:	205 tons surfaced
	235 tons submerged
Diving depth:	30 m
Dimensions:	length 39.9 m
	beam 3.14 m
	draft 2.61 m
Propulsion:	2 kerosene engines; 200 hp; surface speed 10 knots
	2 electric motors; 200 hp; underwater speed 8.5 knots
Armament:	1 torpedo in bow torpedo tube
Complement:	22

The submarines were built by the Krupp firm in Germany by the design of R. d'Equevilley-Montjustin; upon completion these submarines sailed from Kiel to Libau.

The *Kambala* was lost in May 1909 during exercises. She was rammed by the battleship *Rostislav.* The *Karp* and *Karas* were scuttled in Sevastopol in 1919. The *Karp* was recovered in 1925, but was not restored to service.

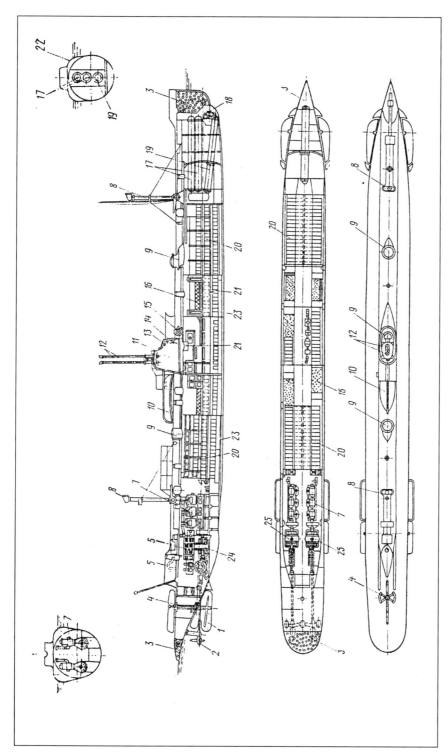

Karp class. 1. vertical rudder; 2. screw propeller; 3. cork filler; 4. axial of the vertical rudder; 5. muffler pipe; 6. main electric station; 7. kerosene engine; 8. ventilation pipes; 9. entrance hatch; 10. boats; 11. main command post; 12. periscope; 13. conning light; 14. control for the vertical rudder; 15. barrel for vertical rudder chain; 16. crew quarters; 17. casing for reserve torpedoes; 18. cover for torpedo apparatus; 19. torpedo apparatus; 20. batteries; 21. inner ballast tanks; 22. tanks in the soft (outer) hull; 23. detachable keels; 24. control post for diving and surfacing; 25. electric engine

The German-built *Karp* at sea.

The three German-built *Karp*-class submarines under way.

Som Class

Name	Built	Name	Built
Som (sheatfish)	1904	*Peskar* (gudgeon)	1905
Shchuka (pike)	1905	*Losos* (salmon)	1905
Sterlyad (sterlet)	1905	*Sudak* (pike perch)	1905
Beluga (white sturgeon)	1905		

Displacement:	105 tons surfaced
	122 tons submerged
Diving depth:	30 m
Dimensions:	length 20.0 m
	beam 3.5 m
	draft 2.9 m
Propulsion:	1 gasoline engine; 160 hp; surface speed 8.5 knots
	1 electric motor; 70 hp; underwater speed 6.0 knots
Armament:	1 torpedo in bow torpedo tube (during the war these submarines were fitted with 1 37-mm gun, except for the *Losos* and *Sudak*)
Complement:	22

The submarine *Som* was purchased when completed from the American firm Holland, with the remainder being built by the Nevskiy Shipbuilding & Machine Works in St. Petersburg to the Holland design No. 7. The *Som* was originally named the *Fulton*.

The *Som* was lost in 1916; the *Shchuka, Peskar, Sterlyad,* and *Beluga* were captured by Germany following the occupation of Revel in 1918.[6] The *Losos* and *Sudak* were scuttled in Sevastopol in 1919.

6. Now the city of Tallinn in Estonia.

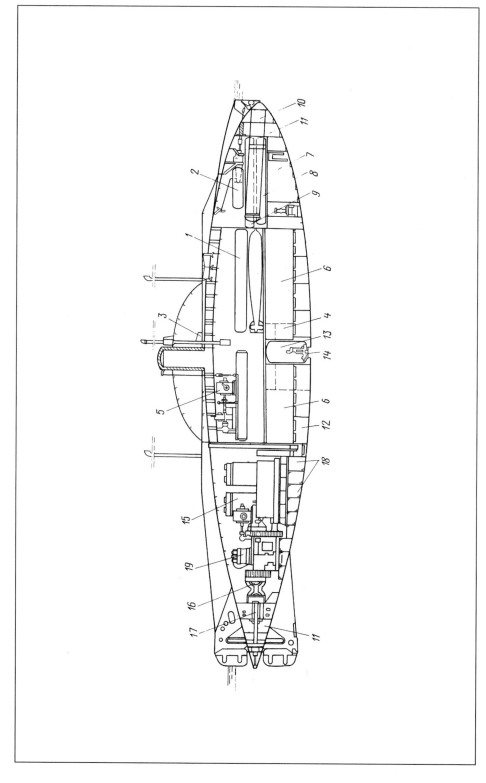

Som. 1., 8., and 9. reservoir for high air pressure; 2. secondary torpedo tank; 3. compass; 4. main ballast tank; 5. hold pump (air compressor); 6. battery; 7. fuel tank; 10. torpedo apparatus; 11. trim tank; 12. equalizing tank; 13. and 18. auxiliary tank; 14. Kingston device; 15. gasoline engine; 16. coupling; 17. thrust bearing; 19. propeller engine

A *Som*-class submarine in dry dock.

A Holland-designed submarine of the *Som* class. These submarines had a "teardrop"-type hull of the same style as the USS *Albacore* (AGSS 569) of the 1950s.

The *Som*-class submarine *Sterlyad*.

The *Sterlyad*.

The *Losos* of the *Som* class with some of her crew in whites—not a practical uniform in the cramped, oily quarters of a submarine.

Osetr Class

Name	Built	Name	Built
Osetr (sturgeon)	1903	*Paltus* (halibut)	1905
Kefal (mullet)	1905	*Bychok* (goby)	1905
Plotva (roach)	1905	*Sig* (whitefish)	1906

Displacement: 153 tons surfaced
187 tons submerged
Diving depth: 30 m
Dimensions: length 22.0 m
beam 3.6 m
draft 3.7 m
Propulsion: 2 gasoline engines; 120 hp; surface speed 8 knots
2 electric motors; 65 hp; underwater speed 4 knots
Armament: 3 torpedoes in 2 bow + 1 stern torpedo tubes
Complement: 24

The submarines of the *Osetr* class were purchased from the American firm Lake; the lead submarine was originally named *Protector*. The *Kefal, Plotva, Paltus, Bychok,* and *Sig* were built at the Newport News Shipbuilding and Dry Dock Company in Virginia and completed in temporary workshops built by the firm in Libau.[7]

The *Osetr, Kefal, Plotva, Paltus,* and *Bychok* were decommissioned in 1913; the *Sig* in 1914.

7. Libau is now the city of Liepãja in Latvia.

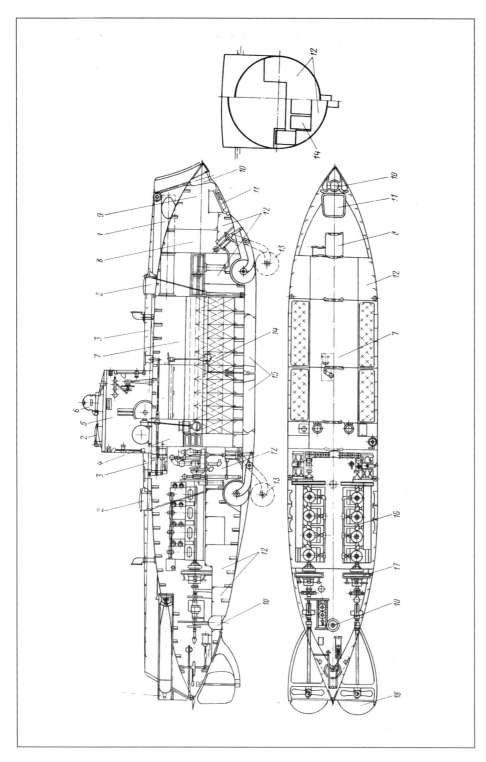

Osetr class. 1. mine apparatus; 2. entrance hatch; 3. fuel tank; 4. galley; 5. main command post; 6. command tower; 7. living quarters; 8. air (lock) chamber; 9. diving chamber; 10. chamber for the submerged anchor; 11. hatch to the diving compartment; 12. ballast tank; 13. wheel; 14. battery; 15. drop-down keel (detachable); 16. gas engine; 17. propeller shaft; 18. horizontal rudder

The *Osetr* in her original configuration as the *Protector* in American waters. (U.S. Navy photo, courtesy of the Naval Historical Center)

A contemporary cutaway drawing of the *Protector*, showing the internal arrangement and the (retracted) bottom-running wheels. (Mariners' Museum, Newport News, Va.)

Osetr-class submarines being fitted out at Libau; the openings for their bow torpedo tubes are evident.

The *Osetr* under way.

The *Osetr* on Russian trials. (Mariners' Museum, Newport News, Va.)

The *Osetr* with a tarpaulin rigged around her conning tower.
Note the height of her mast and periscopes.

The *Osetr*-class submarine *Paltus* on a mirror-smooth sea.

The *Sig*, last of six submarines of the *Osetr* class, moving at high speed.

6-15-04

Osetr-class submarines for the Russian Navy being assembled at Newport News Shipbuilding and Dry Dock Company in Virginia. These were the first submarines built by Newport News. (Newport News Shipbuilding)

An American-built submarine of the *Osetr* class being assembled and fitted out at Libau. (Mariners' Museum, Newport News, Va.)

Minoga

Name	Built
Minoga (lamprey)	1909

Displacement:	123 tons surfaced
	152 tons submerged
Diving depth:	50 m
Dimensions:	length 32.6 m
	beam 2.75 m
	draft 2.75 m
Propulsion:	2 diesel engines; 120 hp; surface speed 11 knots
	1 electric motor; 70 hp; underwater speed 5 knots
Armament:	2 torpedoes in 2 bow torpedo tubes
	1 machine gun (during the war the submarine was fitted with 1 37-mm gun)
Complement:	22

The *Minoga* was the first submarine to be fitted with a diesel engine. She was built by the Baltic Shipbuilding & Engine Works in St. Petersburg to the design of I. G. Bubnov.

The submarine was decommissioned in 1925.

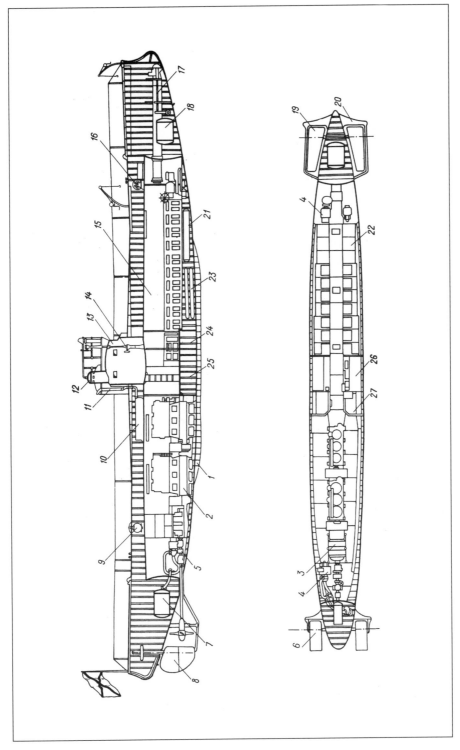

Minoga. 1. lead keel; 2. diesel engine; 3. propeller engine; 4. centrifugal pumps; 5. thrust bearing; 6. stern horizontal rudders; 7. stern trim tank; 8. vertical rudder; 9. rescue buoy; 10. muffler; 11. exhaust pipe; 12. conning tower hatch; 13. main command post; 14. control for vertical rudder; 15. bow compartment; 16. winch; 17. torpedo apparatus; 18. bow trim tank; 19. bow horizontal rudder; 20. rudder fairing; 21. air storage; 22. accumulator; 23. air storage for tank blowing; 24. middle blow tank; 25. middle blow tank; 26. officers' quarters; 27. fuel tanks

The *Minoga*, the first Russian submarine fitted with diesel engines.

Pochtovy

Name	Built
Pochtovy	1907

Displacement:	134 tons surfaced
	146 tons submerged
Diving depth:	30 m
Dimensions:	length 36.0 m
	beam 3.2 m
	draft 2.7 m
Propulsion:	2 gasoline engines; 130 hp; surface speed 11.4 knots/underwater speed 6.2 knots (with one engine)
Armament:	4 torpedoes in external Dzhevetskiy drop-collar torpedo launchers
Complement:	24

The submarine was fitted with a single engine to provide propulsive power for both surface and submerged operation. She was built by the Metallicheskiy Works in St. Petersburg to the design of S. K. Dzhevetskiy.

Compressed air stored under the pressure of 200 atmospheres was used for the underwater operation of the gasoline engine. A pneumatic gas pump forced exhaust gases into a perforated pipe through which the gases were ejected into the water as small bubbles.

The submarine was decommissioned in 1913.

The *Pochtovy* with many more than her crew on the pier; there is an empty drop-collar torpedo launcher alongside the diminutive sail structure.

The *Pochtovy* was fitted with a single engine to provide propulsive power on the surface and submerged. Note the position of the craft's single propeller, behind the after control surfaces.

Alligator Class

Name	Built
Alligator	1911
Kaiman (caiman)	1911
Drakon (dragon)	1911
Krokodil (crocodile)	1911

Displacement:	409 tons surfaced
	480 tons submerged
Diving depth:	50 m
Dimensions:	length 41.0 m
	beam 3.7 m
	draft 4.9 m
Propulsion:	2 gasoline engines; 400 hp; surface speed 8.4 knots
	2 electric motors; 200 hp; underwater speed 7 knots
Armament:	2 torpedoes in 2 bow torpedo tubes
	2 torpedoes in external Dzhevetskiy drop-collar torpedo launchers (during the war, the *Alligator, Kaiman,* and *Krokodil* were fitted with 1 47-mm gun; the *Drakon* with 1 37-mm gun)
Complement:	34

These submarines were built to the design of, and under the guidance of, the Lake firm at the Joint Stock Company Crighton & Company in St. Petersburg. The submarines had numerous faults, and alterations were carried out in Revel under the guidance of the special commission of Russian submariners.

In the fall of 1916 the submarines of the *Alligator* class were deleted from the fleet and laid up. In 1918 they were captured by Germany after the occupation of Revel.

The Lake-designed *Alligator*, lead ship of Simon Lake's second class of submarines built for the Russian Navy. These undersea craft suffered a number of problems.

The *Drakon* of the *Alligator* class under way at high speed.

Akula

Name	Built
Akula (shark)	1911

Displacement:	370 tons surfaced
	468 tons submerged
Diving depth:	50 m
Dimensions:	length 56.0 m
	beam 3.7 m
	draft 3.4 m
Propulsion:	3 diesel engines; 300 hp; surface speed 10.65 knots
	1 electric motor; 300 hp; underwater speed 6.4 knots
Armament:	4 torpedoes in 2 bow + 2 stern torpedo tubes
	4 torpedoes in external Dzhevetskiy drop-collar torpedo launchers
	1 machine gun (during the war 1 47-mm gun was fitted)
Complement:	34

The *Akula* was built by the Baltic Shipbuilding & Engine Works in St. Petersburg to the design of I. G. Bubnov.

On 27 November 1915, the *Akula* left on a mission with four mines on her deck to plant a mine barrier on the sea routes from Libau to Memel and never came back. She probably fell victim to one of the German minefields in the area.

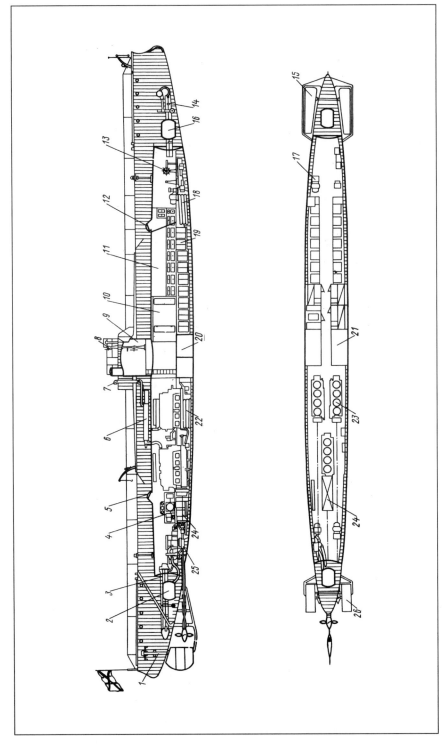

Akula. 1. axial of vertical rudder; 2. stern trim tank; 3. stern torpedo apparatus; 4. main electric station; 5. stern hatch for loading torpedoes; 6. muffler; 7. exhaust pipe; 8. control for vertical rudder; 9. main command post; 10. officers' living quarters; 11. bow compartment; 12. bow hatch for loading torpedoes; 13. control for the horizontal bow rudders; 14. bow torpedo apparatus; 15. horizontal bow rudders; 16. bow trim tank; 17. hold pump; 18. air storage for blowing the ballast tanks; 19. batteries; 20. middle ballast tanks; 21. fuel tanks; 22. air storage for starting the diesel and torpedo firing; 23. diesel engine; 24. propeller engine; 25. thrust bearing; 26. stern horizontal rudders

Bubnov and his triple-screw submarine *Akula*. (U.S. Naval Historical Center)

A view of the torpedo apparatus on the *Akula*.

Krab

Name	Built
Krab	1915

Displacement:	533 tons surfaced
	740 tons submerged
Diving depth:	50 m
Dimensions:	length 53.0 m
	beam 4.25 m
	draft 4.0 m
Propulsion:	4 diesel engines; 300 hp; surface speed 11 knots
	2 electric motors; 330 hp, underwater speed 7.5 knots
Armament:	2 torpedoes in 2 bow torpedo tubes
	1 machine gun
	60 mines
Complement:	50

This was the world's first dedicated minelaying submarine. The *Krab* was built by the Chantier Naval Shipyard in Nikolayev to the design of M. P. Nalyotov.

The boat was scuttled in Sevastopol in 1919. In 1935 she was salvaged but not returned to service

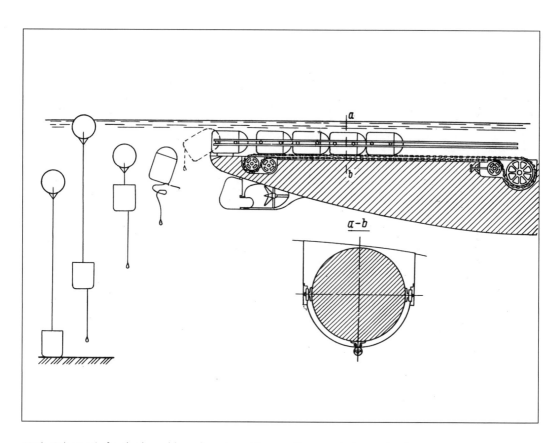

Krab. Schematic for the launching of a mine with a continuous chain mechanism.

The *Krab,* starboard side.

Loading a mine into the stern-opening mine tunnels of the *Krab*.

Holland Submarines Design 27B

Name	Built
No. 1	1914
No. 2	1914
No. 3	1914

Displacement:	33.1 tons surfaced
	43.6 tons submerged
Diving depth:	50 m
Dimensions:	length 20.5 m
	beam 2.3 m
	draft 1.8 m
Propulsion:	1 diesel engine; 50 hp; surface speed 8 knots
	1 electric motor; 35 hp; underwater speed 6 knots
Armament:	2 torpedoes in 2 bow torpedo tubes
Complement:	4

These submarines were built by the Nevskiy Shipbuilding & Machine Works in St. Petersburg to the Holland 27B design.

Submarine *No. 1* was decommissioned in 1918, *No. 2* sank in 1915 in the White Sea, and *No. 3* was left in disrepair on the Danube in Rumania in February 1918.

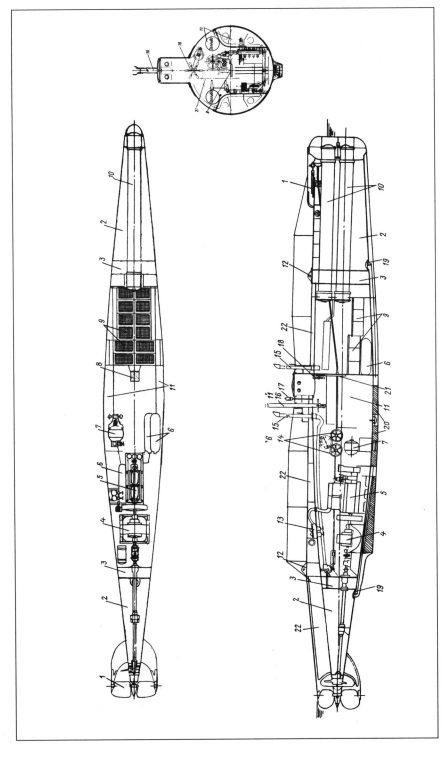

Holland-27B. 1. horizontal rudders; 2. main bow and stern ballast tanks; 3. bow and stern trim tanks; 4. electric engine; 5. diesel engine; 6. air storage; 7. electrical motor for the hold pump; 8. end for the vertical rudder; 9. batteries; 10. torpedo apparatus; 11. auxiliary and fuel tanks; 12. rings for hoisting the submarine; 13. muffler; 14. control for the horizontal rudders; 15. ventilation pipes; 16. periscope; 17. tifon; 18. control for the vertical rudder; 19. Kingston devices for the main ballast tanks; 20. droppable keel; 21. door to the battery compartment; 22. superstructure

No. 1, No. 2, and *No. 3* on railroad cars.

Svyatoi Georgy

Name	Built
Svyatoi Georgy (St. George)	1916

Displacement:	260 tons surfaced
	313 tons submerged
Diving depth:	40 m
Dimensions:	length 45.2 m
	beam 4.2 m
	draft 3.0 m
Propulsion:	2 diesel engines; 360 hp; surface speed 13.4 knots
	2 electric motors; 200 hp; underwater speed 8.25 knots
Armament:	2 torpedoes in 2 bow torpedo tubes
Complement:	24

The *Svyatoi Georgy* was built at the Fiat San Giorgio firm in La Spezia, Italy, to the design of Laurenti.

She was laid up in 1921 and scrapped in 1924.

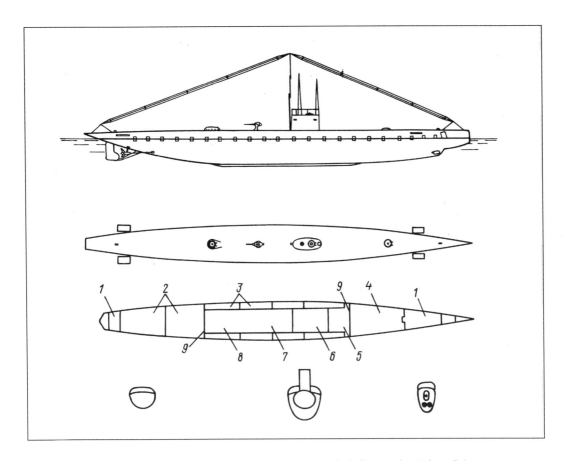

Svyatoi Georgy. 1. trim tanks; 2. battery compartments; 3. main ballast tanks; 4. bow living quarters; 5. compressor compartment; 6. main post; 7. diesel engine compartment; 8. electric engine compartment; 9. high-pressure bulkheads

The Italian-designed and built *Svyatoi Georgy*.

Morzh Class

Name	Built
Morzh (walrus)	1915
Tyulen (seal)	1915
Nerpa (seal)	1915

Displacement:	630 tons surfaced
	758 tons submerged
Diving depth:	50 m
Dimensions:	length 67.0 m
	beam 4.47 m
	draft 3.91 m
Propulsion:	2 diesel engines; 250 hp; surface speed 12 knots
	2 electric motors; 450 hp; underwater speed 8.5 knots
Armament:	4 torpedoes in 2 bow + 2 stern torpedo tubes
	8 torpedoes in external Dzhevetskiy drop-collar torpedo launchers
	1 57-mm gun and 1 47-mm gun on *Nerpa* and *Morzh;* 1 76-mm gun and 1 57-mm gun on *Tyulen*
	1 machine gun
Complement:	33

These submarines were built by the Baltic Works subsidiary in Nikolayev to a Bubnov design.

The *Morzh* was lost in 1917, failing to return from a mission to the Bosporus area; the *Tyulen* was interned by France in Bizerta in 1920; the *Nerpa* was decommissioned in 1930.

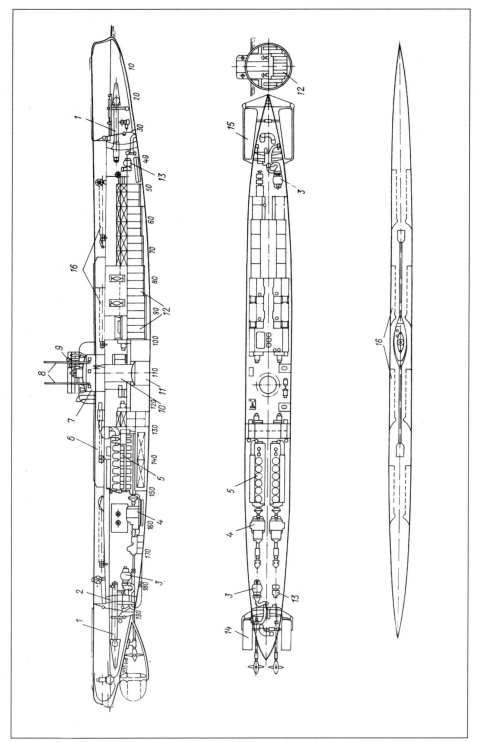

Morzh class. 1. torpedo apparatus; 2. trim tank; 3. centrifugal pump; 4. electric propeller engine; 5. diesel engine; 6. tank; 7. main command post; 8. periscopes; 9. removable compass; 10. equalizing tank; 11. middle (separating) tank; 12. battery; 13. electric compressor; 14. stern horizontal rudders; 15. bow horizontal rudders; 16. torpedo dropping device

The conning tower of a submerged *Morzh*-class submarine alongside a sister submarine.

The *Nerpa* of the *Morzh* class at launching. Note the size and shape of her rudder.

The *Morzh* in dry dock; note the spaces for the drop-collar torpedo launchers.

The submarine *Morzh* under way.

Narval Class

Name	Built
Narval (narwhal)	1915
Kit (whale)	1915
Kashalot (sperm whale)	1916

Displacement:	621 tons surfaced
	994 tons submerged
Diving depth:	50 m
Dimensions:	length 70.0 m
	beam 6.6 m
	draft 3.5 m
Propulsion:	4 diesel engines; 160 hp; surface speed 13 knots
	2 electric motors; 490 hp; underwater speed 9.8 knots
Armament:	4 torpedoes in 2 bow + 2 stern torpedo tubes
	8 torpedoes in external Dzhevetskiy drop-collar torpedo launchers on *Narval* and *Kit;* 4 on *Kashalot*
	1 75-mm gun
	1 57-mm gun
	2 machine guns
Complement:	33

These submarines were built by the Nevskiy subsidiary in Nikolayev to the Holland design 31A.

The *Narval, Kit,* and *Kashalot* were scuttled in Sevastopol in 1919. The *Kit* was raised in 1935 and scrapped.

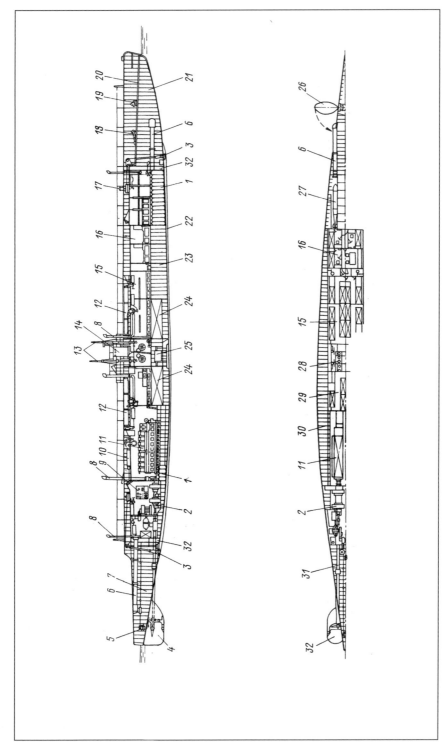

Narval class. 1. air storage; 2. propeller engines; 3. submerged anchors; 4. vertical rudder; 5. drive for the vertical rudder; 6. tubular torpedo apparatus; 7. stern ballast tanks; 8. ventilating pipes; 9. main electric station; 10. muffler; 11. diesel motors; 12. rotary torpedo apparatus; 13. periscopes; 14. main command post; 15. ward room and mess room; 16. commander's quarters; 17. capstan; 18. anchor; 19. drive for the horizontal rudders; 20. watertight deck; 21. bow ballast tanks; 22. keel; 23. fuel tank; 24. battery; 25. equalizing tanks; 26. bow horizontal rudders; 27. reserve torpedoes; 28. main command post; 29. officers' quarters; 30. between-hull ballast tanks; 31. propeller shaft; 32. trim tanks

The *Narval* off Sevastopol, showing one of her large bow diving planes in the stowed position.

The *Narval*-class submarine *Kashalot* at launching at Nikolayev.

The *Narval* being launched in Nikolayev on the Black Sea.

Bars Class

Name	Built	Name	Built
Bars (snow leopard)	1915	*Edinorog* (narwhal)	1917
Gepard (hunting leopard)	1915	*Yaguar* (jaguar)	1917
Vepr (wild boar)	1915	*Zmeya* (snake)	1917
Volk (wolf)	1916	*Kuguar* (cougar)	1917
Tigr (tiger)	1916	*Ugor* (eel)	1917
Lvitsa (lioness)	1916	*Ersh* (rockfish)	1917
Rys (lynx)	1916	*Gagara* (loon)	1917
Pantera (panther)	1916	*Utka* (duck)	1917
Leopard	1916	*Burevestnik* (petrel)	1917
Tur (urus)	1917	*Orlan* (sea eagle)	1917

Displacement:	650 tons surfaced
	780 tons submerged
Diving depth:	50 m
Dimensions:	length 67.97 m
	beam 4.47 m
	draft 3.94 m
Propulsion:	2 diesel engines; 250 hp; surface speed 11.5 knots
	2 electric motors; 450 hp; underwater speed 8.5 knots except *Ugor* and *Ersh*
	2 diesel engines; 420 hp; surface speed 13 knots
	2 electric motors; 450 hp; underwater speed 8.5 knots *Zmeya* and *Kuguar*
	2 diesel engines; 1,320 hp; surface speed 17 knots
	2 electric motors; 450 hp; underwater speed 8.5 knots
Armament:	4 torpedoes in 2 bow + 2 stern torpedo tubes except *Ersh*
	8 torpedoes in external Dzhevetskiy drop-collar torpedo launchers, except 4 in *Burevestnik, Orlan, Lebed,* and *Pelikan*
	4 external, collapsible Lessner-built torpedo launchers in *Yaguar*
	Ersh, which was refitted during construction into a minelayer, had 2 torpedoes in 2 bow torpedo tubes and 42 mines
	1 75-mm gun and 1 57-mm gun in *Tigr, Rys, Pantera,* and *Leopard*
	2 57-mm guns in *Vepr* and *Volk*
	1 57-mm gun in *Kuguar* and *Zmeya*
	1 37-mm gun in *Gagara* and *Utka*
	all carried 1 machine gun
Complement:	33

The *Bars* class was designed by Bubnov; the builders were the following firms:

- Baltic Shipbuilding & Engine Works in St. Petersburg (*Bars, Gepard, Vepr, Volk, Ugor, Ersh,* and *Forel*)
- Baltic Works subsidiary in Nikolayev (*Gagara* and *Utka*)
- Nobel & Lessner in Revel (*Tigr, Lvitsa, Rys, Pantera, Leopard, Tur, Edinorog, Yaguar, Zmeya, Kuguar,* and *Yaz*)
- Chantier Naval in Nikolayev (*Burevestnik, Orlan, Lebed,* and*Pelikan*)

Three submarines of this class were not completed:the *Forel, Yaz* (ide), *Lebed* (swan), and *Pelikan*.

The *Bars, Gepard,* and *Lvitsa* were lost in 1917 in the Baltic Sea; the *Edinorog* sank in 1918 during the "ice cruise" from Helsingfors to Kronshtadt. The *Gagara* and *Utka* were interned by France in 1920 in Bizerta. The *Vepr, Ugor,* and *Kuguar* were decommissioned in 1922; the *Volk, Zmeya,* and *Tigr* in 1935. The *Rys* sank in 1935 and was salvaged the same year without restoration. The *Leopard* and *Tur* were decommissioned in 1940; the *Pantera* in 1955.

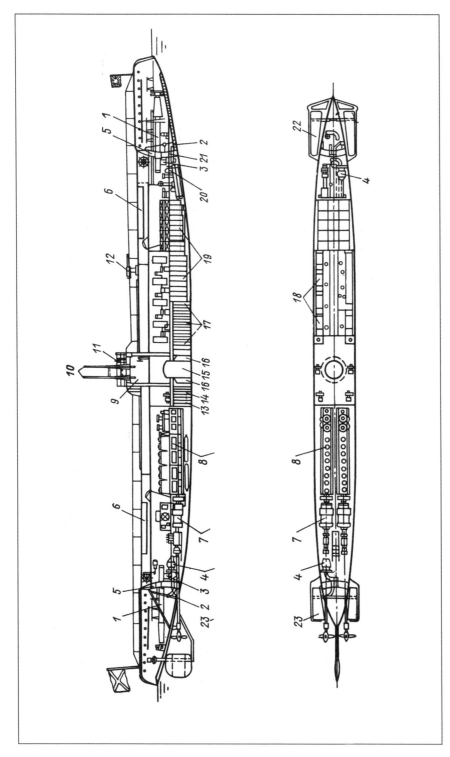

Bars class. 1. tubular torpedo apparatus; 2. stern and bow submerged anchors; 3. secondary tanks for the submerged anchors; 4. centrifugal pump; 5. trim tanks; 6. torpedo dropping device; 7. main electric propeller engines; 8. main diesel engines; 9. main command post; 10. periscopes; 11. control wheel for vertical rudders; 12. binnacle for the removable compass; 13. oil tank; 14. secondary tank; 15. equalizing tank; 16. "separator" tank; 17. fuel tank; 18. ward rooms; 19. batteries; 20. compressor; 21. fresh water tank; 22. bow horizontal rudders; 23. stern horizontal rudders

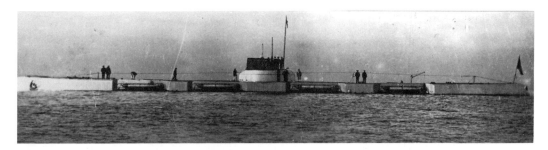

The *Bars*, lead submarine of the largest class of submarines built in this century for the Tsarist Navy.

Details of the *Bars*-class submarine *Volk* alongside a depot ship; note the cluttered conning tower and the Dzhevetsky drop-collar torpedo launchers. The *Volk* was one of the top-scoring tsarist submarines.

The *Bars*-class submarine *Ersh* at the Baltic Works in Petrograd immediately before launching in 1917. (U.S. Naval Historical Center)

Two submarines of the *Bars* class under construction about 1914. (Boris V. Drashpil via U.S. Naval Historical Center)

The *Bars*-class minelaying submarine *Ersh* as launched. (U.S. Naval Historical Center)

The *Peskar* (foreground), *Alligator, Bars,* and *Gepard* alongside the rescue and depot ship *Volkhov* in 1915.

The *Bars* at sea.

Closeup of a *Bars*-class submarine showing torpedo drop collars. (Boris V. Drashpil via U.S. Naval Historical Center)

Closeup of a *Bars*-class submarine with the torpedo drop-collars plated over.

Caught in ice, from left: *Volk*, *Bars*, and *Gepard*.

The *Leopard* under way; note the bow anchor, fitted port and starboard in these submarines.

The *Bars*-class submarine *Kuguar,* with a ventilator rigged aft of the superstructure.

The *Bars*-class submarine *Tigr* with apparently her entire crew on deck for the photographer.

The ice-encrusted *Yaguar* and *Leopard* of the *Bars* class, 1916.

After fleeing to Bizerta in French North Africa during the Russian Civil War, numerous Russian warships—including submarines—were abandoned. This photograph was taken in 1926.

The end of several tsarist submarines in Bizerta in 1920: The tsarist destroyer *Bezpokoini* and three submarines are shown in the port, a refuge for much of the tsarist fleet after the Bolshevik victory in the Russian Civil War. (Boris V. Drashpil via U.S. Naval Historical Center)

AG (American Holland) Class

Name	Built	Name	Built
AG-11	1916	*AG-14*	1916
AG-12	1916	*AG-15*	1916
AG-13	1916		

Displacement:	355 tons surfaced
	433 tons submerged
Diving depth:	50 m
Dimensions:	length 46.0 m
	beam 4.88 m
	draft 3.8 m
Propulsion:	2 diesel engines; 240 hp; surface speed 13 knots
	2 electric motors; 160 hp; underwater speed 10.5 knots
Armament:	4 torpedoes in 4 bow torpedo tubes
Complement:	30

Eleven submarines of this design were built by the Holland firm in the United States. They were built in sections that were shipped to Vladivostok in 1916; from there five submarines, the *AG-11* through *AG-15*, were shipped by railway to St. Petersburg for assembly by the Baltic Shipbuilding & Engine Works; six units (*AG-21* through *AG-26*) went by rail to the Baltic Works subsidiary in Nikolayev for assembly.

The *AG-21* and *AG-22* were completed but not placed in commission by the Imperial Navy. The submarines *AG-23* through *AG-26* were not completed until after the Revolution. Four other units—the *AG-17* through *AG-20*—were not delivered to Russia but were completed for the U.S. Navy.

The *AG-14* was lost in the Baltic Sea in 1917; the *AG-11, AG-12, AG-13,* and *AG-15* were blown up in Hango (Finland) on 6 April 1918, together with the base Oland to prevent their capture by Germans. The *AG-21* was scuttled in Sevastopol in 1919 (raised in 1928 and restored to service in 1930). The *AG-22* fled to Bizerta and was interned by France.

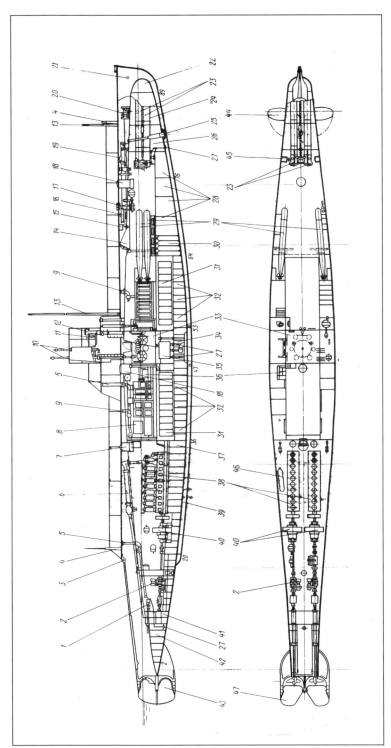

AG-11 Holland class. 1. steering mechanism; 2. air compressors; 3. ring for hoisting the submarine; 4. end posts; 5. ventilators; 6. muffler; 7. engine compartment hatch; 8. electrical switch board; 9. ballast tank ventilation valves; 10. periscopes; 11. upper hatch of the main command post; 12. conning tower post; 13. masts; 14. hatch for the loading of torpedoes; 15. signal buoy with a telephone; 16. and 17. capstans for the submerged and surface anchors; 18. exit hatch; 19. surface anchor; 20. drive for the bow horizontal rudders; 21. tow ring; 22. front cover of the torpedo tubes; 23. torpedo apparatus; 24. bow trim tank; 25. submerged anchor; 26., 32., and 42. main ballast tanks; 27. Kingston devices; 28. fuel tanks; 29. reserve torpedoes; 30. and 46. tanks for compressed air; 31. battery; 33. control room; 34. auxiliary tank; 35. equalizing tank; 36. electric galley; 37. lubricating oil tank; 38. diesel engines; 39. keel; 40. main electric motor; 41. stern trim tank; 43. vertical rudder; 44. bow horizontal rudders; 45. apparatus for underwater signaling; 46. stern horizontal rudders; 48. footways

An AG-series submarine, designed by John P. Holland. Tsarist Russia procured submarines from Holland and Simon Lake, the competitive American submarine designers of the turn of the century.

The Holland-type submarine *AG-14* flying the flag of St. Andrews, which was used by the Tsarist Navy and the post–Cold War Russian Navy.

E-1 Class (British)

Name	Built
E-1	1912
E-8	1913

Displacement: 655 tons surfaced
796 tons submerged

Diving depth:

Dimensions: length 54.2 m
beam   6.9 m
draft   3.8 m

Propulsion: 2 diesel engines; 800 hp; surface speed 15 knots
2 electric motors; 420 hp; underwater speed 9 knots

Armament: 4 torpedoes in 1 bow + 2 side + 1 stern torpedo tubes
2 reload torpedoes
1 6-pounder or 4-inch (102-mm) gun

Complement: 30

The *E-1* and *E*-8 submarines were built by the naval dockyard in Chatam. In October 1914 they broke into the Baltic Sea to operate with the Russian Navy. Both submarines were blown up by their British crews on 3 April 1918 at outer roads (Sveaborg, Finland) to prevent their capture by Germans.

These submarines were similar in appearance to the later *E*-9 class.

E-9 Class (British)

Name	Built
E-9	1913
E-18	1915
E-19	1915

Displacement:	667 tons surfaced
	807 tons submerged
Diving depth:	
Dimensions:	length 55.2 m
	beam 4.6 m
	draft 3.8 m
Propulsion:	2 diesel engines; 800 hp; surface speed 15 knots
	2 electric motors; 420 hp; underwater speed 9 knots
Armament:	5 torpedoes in 2 bow + 2 side + 1 stern torpedo tubes
	2 reload torpedoes
	1 6-pounder or 4-inch (102-mm) gun
Complement:	30

The *E-9, E-18,* and *E-19* were built by the Vickers Works.

In August–September 1915 the submarines broke into the Baltic Sea to operate with the Russian Navy. They were blown up by their crews on 3 April 1918, at the outer roads of Sveaborg (Finland) to prevent capture by the Germans.

The *E-13* was also to participate in combat operations in the Baltic Sea, but she could not break into the area and was captured in Denmark.

A British E-boat—in dazzle camouflage—at Revel while assigned to the Russian Baltic Fleet.

The British submarine *E-18*.

Ice was a major problem for submarines in the Gulf of Finland for much of the year. This is the conning tower of the British *E-9*. (Royal Navy Submarine Museum)

C Class (British)

Name	Built
C-26	1909
C-27	1909
C-32	1909
C-35	1909

Displacement:	290 tons surfaced
	320 tons submerged
Diving depth:	
Dimensions:	length 43.3 m
	beam 4.1 m
	draft 3.5 m
Propulsion:	1 gasoline engine; 600 hp; surface speed 13 knots
	1 electric motor; 300 hp; underwater speed 7.5 knots
Armament:	2 torpedoes in 2 bow torpedo tubes
	2 reload torpedoes
Complement:	16

These submarines were built by the Vickers Works.

They came to Russia via the Northern route and were delivered to Arkhangelsk. From there, they were shipped on barges along the river system, arriving in Kronshtadt in the fall of 1916.

After operations in the Baltic area, on 3–5 April 1918 they were blown up by their crews at the outer roads of Sveaborg (Finland) to prevent their capture by the Germans.

The British *C-32* moving by barge from the Arctic to Petrograd. (Royal Navy Submarine Museum)

❖ Index ❖

❧ About the Authors ❧

I. D. Spassky, a graduate of the Higher Naval Engineering School in Leningrad, served in the Soviet Navy after World War II, earning an advanced degree in engineering, and was assigned to submarine design work at the Central Design Bureau No. 18. As part of the Khrushchev-era cutbacks in the armed forces, he was discharged in 1955 and transferred to the reserves as a lieutenant commander. He continued to work at Central Design Bureau No. 18, now known as "Rubin," rising to the positions of head and general designer of that prestigious organization. He is also the Academician of the Russian Academy of Sciences.

V. P. Semyonov, a graduate of the Leningrad Institute for Shipbuilding, joined the Central Design Bureau No. 18 in 1947. He worked on such advanced-technology submarines as Projects 615 (Quebec), 617 (Whale), and 658 (Hotel). He was deputy to Academician S. N. Kovalev, the chief designer of the Project 667 (Yankee and Delta) series and Project 941 (Typhoon) strategic missile submarines, the last being the largest undersea craft ever built. Semyonov now heads the Submarine Building History Bureau of Rubin.

Norman Polmar, an internationally known naval analyst and author, is the author of several books on submarines as well as the Naval Institute's reference books *Guide to the Soviet Navy* and *The Ships and Aircraft of the U.S. Fleet.* He is coauthor with Jurrien Noot of *Submarines of the Russian and Soviet Navies, 1719–1990* (Naval Institute, 1991). He has been a frequent guest of the Rubin design bureau in St. Petersburg.